THE FRANK LOESSER SONGBOOK

WITH A PREFACE BY Richard Rodgers

AND TEXT BY Cynthia Lindsay

ILLUSTRATED BY Paul Bacon

SIMON AND SCHUSTER

NEW YORK

PUBLISHED BY SIMON AND SCHUSTER

ROCKEFELLER CENTER, 630 FIFTH AVENUE

NEW YORK, NEW YORK 10020

FIRST PRINTING

SBN 671-20893-4

LIBRARY OF CONGRESS CATALOG CARD NUMBER: 78-156157

MANUFACTURED IN THE UNITED STATES OF AMERICA

PRINTED BY THE MURRAY PRINTING COMPANY, FORGE VILLAGE, MASS.

PREFACE

How easy it is to have a deep appreciation of Frank Loesser's work, and how difficult it is to explain why. Its extraordinary quality cannot lie in individual notes or syllables, or even in their juxtaposition within a phrase or a number of phrases. This would be as appropriate as saying that his wife, Jo, is attractive because her face is four inches from lower eyebrow to tip of chin. Better to settle for the fact that she is very pretty and Frank's songs are wonderful.

Some years ago, my wife returned from the village near us in Connecticut and brought me a recording of a song that was not familiar to me. It was "Baby, It's Cold Outside." I listened to it and jumped up from my chair to phone Frank in California and say I thought it was one of the finest pieces of song writing I had ever heard. Today I don't care why I thought so; I just know what it did for me and millions of others. Perhaps this sort of emotional response is all any piece needs to become a valid work of art. Certainly the other "art" component (technical-intellectual) is equally important, but certainly it is strongly present in the Loesser pieces. Only a man with strong technical interest and capability could have written "Fugue for Tinhorns" or "Baby, It's Cold Outside," and only a man with strong emotional involvement could have done "My Heart Is So Full of You" or "Joey, Joey, Joey."

The well-tempered songwriter creates his own sort of "scherzo"—not necessarily fast, but surely joyous. It is difficult to listen to "Standing on the Corner" without wanting to giggle, not just at the words but at the music. This gifted man could wander off the conventional thirty-two-bar reservation without getting lost. Thus, "I Believe in You" is a full-fledged operatic aria with a beat. It is also a statement of self-faith. Was Frank singing to himself? He was entitled to do it.

Perhaps you would like a change of pace. There is a sweet, affectionate waltz for you in "Wonderful Copenhagen." Are you in the mood for muscle? You have "Praise the Lord and Pass the Ammunition!" or "What Do You Do in the Infantry." Is your feeling of personal affection a little shy and a bit delicate? Sing "Once in Love with Amy." For the full gamut, sing everything from Guys and Dolls.

Frank Loesser as a man is a book in himself. He was happy; he was strong; he had enormous peaks and frightening depths. This is only to say that he was intensely human. With it all, he was a living refutation of the theory that composers are not very bright. Frank was a first-rate businessman without ever having to resort to tricks. He knew his own value, and he recognized the value of others. With all this came a thorough knowledge of stagecraft that carried him through one successful musical play after another.

After all, you would have to say, "Frank Loesser was a man for all theater seasons."

RICHARD RODGERS

CONTENTS

INTRODUCTION

Nothing ever surprised Frank Loesser. A friend who knew him very early in his career said, "Funny—even before Frank had written anything you knew he would, and you weren't surprised when he did. But neither was he—everything that happened to him he accepted as his due because he simply knew he had it coming to him. Even after he started being given awards he was never excited; he'd just say, 'I thought I should have had it three years ago.' And yet this wasn't conceit; he was without conceit. His taste was perfect and he had to write to his own satisfaction, and I guess that just made it good enough for anybody."

On June 29, 1910, Frank Loesser was born into a family of serious musicians. Loesser bypassed his family's efforts toward formal musical training and got on with it himself. He started improvising on the piano at the age of six, then started composing on the harmonica, winning third prize in a New York harmonica contest along the way. He also bypassed the family's efforts toward formal academic training, whisking through school with natural brilliance and no attention, and left college after one year to do what he wanted to do. He wanted to write songs, and nothing could have stopped him. Extraordinarily, having bypassed formal musical and academic education, Loesser was a serious musician, a Bach scholar, and had an overwhelming fund of knowledge of art, literature, philosophy, the mortise-and-tenon construction of sixteenth-century cabinetry and the mating habits of the redwing blackbird.

The insatiable curiosity, the demand for perfection (nothing was ever good enough—he constantly tore things up), were inseparable in the talent and in the man; he was a giant in both.

Talking with Frank Loesser's friends about him is an extraordinary experience. There are countless anecdotes, and after one someone will say, "That's a Frank!" Particularly about one of his outrageous pieces of nonsense such as constructing with great craftsmanship the corner (just the corner) of a Regency desk, inlaid and perfectly finished. He then sent it to his friend John Steinbeck, a piece of notepaper attached with the printed words FROM THE DESK OF FRANK LOESSER.

There were funny stories, outrageous stories, stories of his enormous generosity, and there were the friends who couldn't talk about him without crying, because he was so many things to so many people and special to each.

And then there was Sidney Kingsley: "In some curious way, Frank was a part of me. I never realized how much of what we do we do for others; for instance, when I write a play, it's people like Frank whom I wish to please. I had so many things I wanted him to see: my studio; a beautiful seventeenth-century room I'm installing; my new play. Everyone, including myself, was amazed at my great emotion at his death. I couldn't understand the depth of my grief until I realized I'd been saving him for a rainy day."

Knowing Frank Loesser was a rare and rewarding experience for many reasons, but the most important was that no matter who and what you were, he made you better. Whether it was your talent, your humor, your confidence in yourself, you came away from him more creative, funnier, more perceptive about yourself and lighter in spirit; a prettier woman, a stronger man; in fact, crazy about yourself because he made you the best of what you were.

C. L.

W ho's that little character swinging his coattails and whistling? I never saw anybody so self-assured."

Hoagy Carmichael was looking out an office window of the Paramount studios in Hollywood in the 1940's. It was his first look at Frank Loesser. He began to watch him scurrying about the lot, primarily back and forth to the commissary for his eleventh, twelfth or thirteenth cup of coffee of the day.

"Watching Frank fascinated me," Carmichael says. "The very cockiness of the kid impressed me. I figured he had something. I was working without a collaborator at the time, so you can imagine my enthusiasm and delight when the head of the music department deposited Frank in my crib.

"At first the kid shook me up—his exuberance and his zany talk were too much for me. Frank didn't seem serious enough about the matter of writing songs. It wasn't the first time I was wrong. After we'd worked together a little while, I realized he'd only been joking with me to keep me happy and alive. Then one day, sitting at the piano, he said, 'How's this?' I said, 'Follow it with this—.' We reeled off a few stanzas, and I realized this was the lyricist I'd hoped he'd be. All the time we worked together, Frank never violated the rules of construction or what it takes to make a hit song. It didn't take any time for me to know he'd justified the confidence I'd had when I first saw him strutting across the lot at Paramount. We had a lot of hits—a lot of laughs!"

And it didn't take any time after that for Loesser to justify his own as well as Carmichael's confidence by turning out one hit song after another, first in collaboration and soon only alone. One of those songs was "Baby, It's Cold Outside"—a song he never meant to publish but wrote for his own amusement and that of his friends, and with which he won the Academy Award for the best motion-picture song of the year.

ON A SLOW BOAT TO CHINA

Slowly with a beat

CHORUS

I'd love to get you ___ on a slow boat to Chi-na, ___

All to my-self ___ a - lone. ___ Get you and

keep you___ in my arms ev-er-more,___ Leave all your lov-ers___ (love-lies)

Weep-ing on the far - a - way shore.___ Out on the brin-y___ with a

moon big and shin-y, Melt - ing your heart___ of stone,___

WHAT ARE YOU DOING NEW YEAR'S EVE

VERSE
Ad lib.

When the bells all ring,_____ and the horns all blow,_____ And the

mp colla voce

couples we know ____ are fond-ly kiss-ing, ____ Will I

be with you, ____ or will I be a-mong the miss-ing? ____

CHORUS
Slowly and sentimentally

May-be it's much too early in the game,

Ah, but I thought I'd ask you just the same:___ What are you do-ing

16

Not fast

With a slow, steady drip

| F | G♭ | F | C7−5−9 | F | G♭ | F | C7−5−9 | F | G♭ |

Bloop,   bleep,   bloop,   bleep,   bloop,

| F | C7−5−9 | G♭9 | F | B♭9 | F | C+9 | F | G♭ |

bleep,   The fau-cet keeps a-drip-ping and I can't sleep.___   Bleep,

bloop,   bleep,   The   fau - cet keeps a - drip-ping and I   just

can't   sleep!

sleep!

I WISH I DIDN'T LOVE YOU SO

Af-ter all this time with-out you, Af-ter all this time, I find That it's

still no use to say to my-self "Out of sight, out of mind."

27

with some new _ ten-der friend, _ Smil-ing by now _ with my heart

on the mend, _ But when I try, Some-thing in that heart says

"No." ____ You're still there. I wish I did-n't love you so. _

29

VERSE

E♭

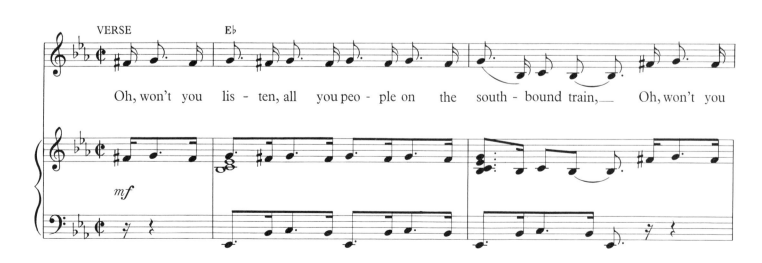

Oh, won't you lis - ten, all you peo - ple on the south - bound train,___ Oh, won't you

TALLAHASSEE

lis - ten to my friend-ly ad - vice? _____ A-bout a quar-ter af - ter sev - en we'll be

pull - ing in - to par - a - dise. _____

34

SPRING WILL BE A LITTLE LATE THIS YEAR

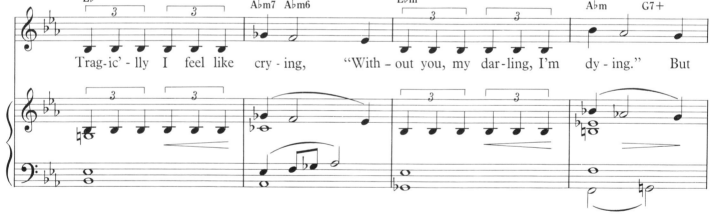

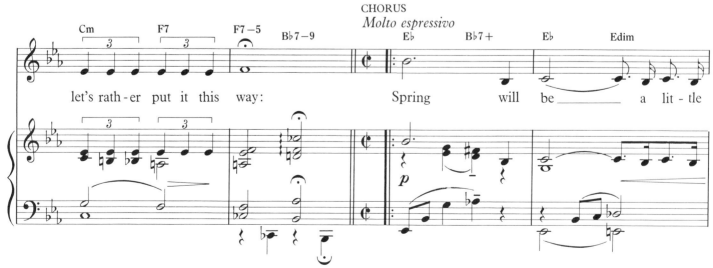

late this year,_____ A lit-tle late ar-riv-ing in
my lone-ly world o-ver here, For you have left me, and
where is our A-pril of old? You have left me, and win-ter con-tin-ues
cold, As if to say Spring will be_____ a lit-tle slow to

(WHERE ARE YOU?) NOW THAT I NEED YOU

Slowly

VERSE
Ad lib.

I called you on the phone last night, and ba-by, you were not there. I tried your door-bell ump-teen times, then walked a-way in de-spair. Then

took too much for grant - ed. _____ I nev - er thought I'd lie a - wake

_ and sigh, Where are you? _____ Now that I need you, ____

_ Now that I love you so mad - ly I could die. _

1

Where

2

Slowly, with feeling

Rose - an - na, Rose - an - na! The wind sings her name, And all night through, all chil - ly night through, She

lit - tle did I cry, Lit - tle did I dream I'd be haunt - ed by Rose -

an - na, Rose - an - na! I love her a - lone, And

now I'll need, I'll ev - er - more need Rose - an - na for my ve - ry

own. Rose - own.

UNIFORM

Throughout his extraordinary career, Frank Loesser has been referred to as everything from "the only instinctive authentic genius in the musical world" to "a cocky [unprintable-in-a-songbook]." Somewhere in between, the phrase "a disciplined pixie" cropped up. It is on the nose. Loesser looked at the world not through rose-colored glasses but with high-powered binoculars, and he found it wanting. He also found it funny — hilariously funny. But he controlled his giggles and channeled them into songs of social commentary which made a serious impact on world culture. Satirical one moment, deeply moving another; touching or tongue-in-cheek; ballad, patter song or march — a Loesser song was at all times the highest form of song writing, because he was incapable of bad taste.

Aside from taste and timing, Loesser had a knack for being in the right place at the right time — including the United States Army. While in service in World War II, he was called by a friend, writer E. J. Kahn, Jr., then a public relations officer for the Infantry. Kahn said, "All the services have their own songs. The Navy has 'Anchors Aweigh'; the Air Force, 'Wild Blue Yonder'; the Marines, 'Halls of Montezuma.' The Infantry has nothing. Think of a song — maybe about a hero." Loesser said, "Get me a hero." Kahn arrived at Loesser's apartment with a long list of brave men with unpronounceable six-syllabled names. Loesser said, "I can't make up rhymes about people with names like that." Then Kahn said, "Got one — how does 'Rodger Young' strike you?" "Done," said Loesser. Loesser created the song; the Infantry created the Combat Infantry Band to play it. The song was played for the first time at Rodger Young's birthplace in Ohio, then on every radio station in the country, and rapidly became one of the great war songs. This was in 1945. What Loesser neglected to mention at the time was that he had already written another war song (the first time he had ever written both words and music), but with his usual instinct for timing, was waiting until American morale was low to release it. It was "Praise the Lord and Pass the Ammunition!"

PRAISE THE LORD  AND PASS THE AMMUNITION!

Martial

VERSE

Down went the gun-ner; a bul-let was his fate.

Down went the gun-ner, and then the gun-ner's mate. Up jumped the sky pi-lot,

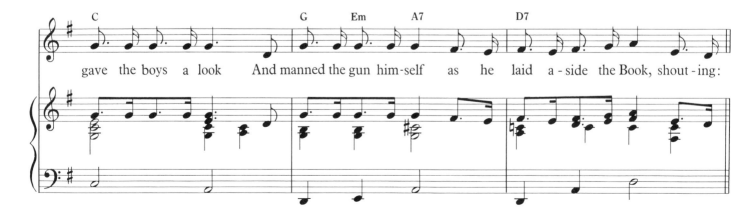

gave the boys a look And manned the gun him-self as he laid a-side the Book, shout-ing:

got to give him cred - it, for a son-of-a-gun of a gun - ner was

he, Shout-ing: "Praise the Lord; we're on a might-y mis-sion.

All a-board! We're not a-go-in' fish-in'. Praise the Lord and

pass the am-mu-ni-tion, and we'll all stay free!" free!"

WHAT DO YOU DO IN THE INFANTRY?

March (regulation Army tempo—120 paces per minute)

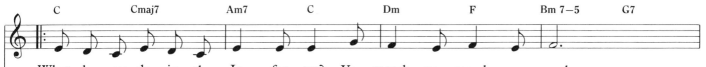

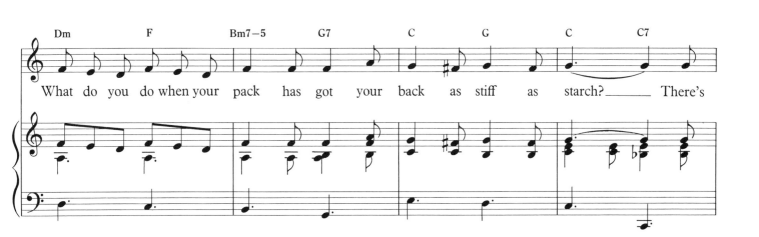

What do you do in the In - fan - try? You march, you march, you march.

What do you do when your pack has got your back as stiff as starch?_____ There's

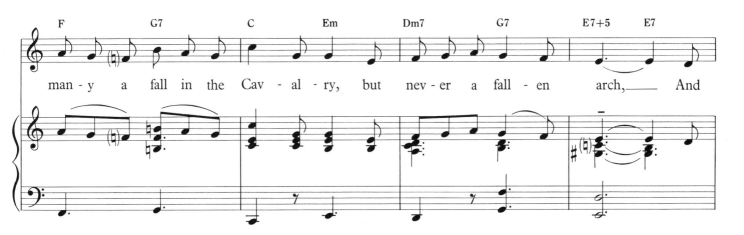

man - y a fall in the Cav - al - ry, but nev - er a fall - en arch,_____ And

what do you do in the In-fan-try? You march, you march, you march!

What do you do in the In-fan-try? You hike, you hike, you hike.

What do you get in the In-fan-try? A left and right o-blique.____ The
(pronounced O-blike)

son-of-a-gun in the Sig-nal Corps is trav-el-ing on a bike,____ And

THE ROAD TO VICTORY

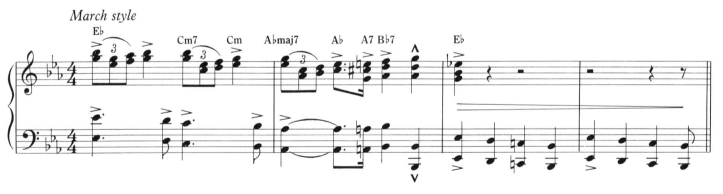

March style

Get on, get on, get on the road to vic-to-ry. Get off, get off, get

FIRST CLASS PRIVATE MARY BROWN

RODGER YOUNG

Moderately, with sincerity

f

rall.

mf a tempo Bb Fm7 Bb7 (6) Bb7 Eb

1. Oh, they've got no time for glo - ry in the In - fan - try,_____
2. (Caught in) am - bush lay a com - pa - ny of ri - fle - men,_____
3. (It was) he who drew the fire_____ of the en - e - my_____
4. (On the) is - land of New Geor - gia in the Sol - o - mons_____
5. (No, they've) got no time for glo - ry in the In - fan - try,_____

mf a tempo

(Guitar tacet) Bb Fm7 Bb7 (6) Bb7 Eb

_____ Oh, they've got no use for prais - es loud - ly sung,_____
_____ Just gre - nades a - gainst ma - chine guns in the gloom,_____
_____ That a com - pa - ny of men might live to fight,_____
_____ Stands a sim - ple wood - en cross a - lone to tell_____
_____ No, they've got no use for prais - es loud - ly sung,_____

Where's Charley?

When the subject of translating a very old-fashioned farce, *Charley's Aunt,* by Brandon Thomas, into a musical comedy for Broadway first came up, experienced heads in the theatrical world said it couldn't be done. They were wrong. *Where's Charley?—* book by George Abbott, words and music by Frank Loesser—was a solid hit.

The show was Frank Loesser's first Broadway musical, and it established him so thoroughly in this medium, he never left it except to take time off to do the film *Hans Christian Andersen.*

It was also the first time a star of a musical comedy had drawn the audience into a song and used said audience as a chorus. No one in any of the many audiences who watched Ray Bolger's irresistible performance as Charley Wykeham and felt themselves drawn into singing "Once in Love with Amy" along with the star will ever forget it.

The show was also a splendid demonstration of Loesser's ability to leap from nonsense, as in "The New Ashmolean Marching Society and Students Conservatory Band," to tenderness, as in "My Darling, My Darling," without apparently even catching his breath.

Once in Love with Amy

Slow and easy soft-shoe

VERSE | G | Gmaj7 | G7 | C | Cm | G

I caught you, sir, hav-ing a look at her As she went stroll-ing

Am7 | D9 | D7 | G | G♯dim | Am7 | D7

by._____ Now, did-n't your heart beat boom, boom, boom, boom, boom And did-n't you

loves a girl and la-ter thinks it o - ver And just quits cold, But

once in love with A -my,__ Al-ways in love with A - my.__ Ev-er and ev-er

sweet -ly you'll ro-mance 'er. Trou-ble is, the an-swer will be_____ That A - my'd rath-er stay in

love with me._____ me._____

69

My Darling, My Darling

Moderato con moto

mf

VERSE
Rubato

F7

Cm7

Till a mo - ment a - go _____ we were

mp

p

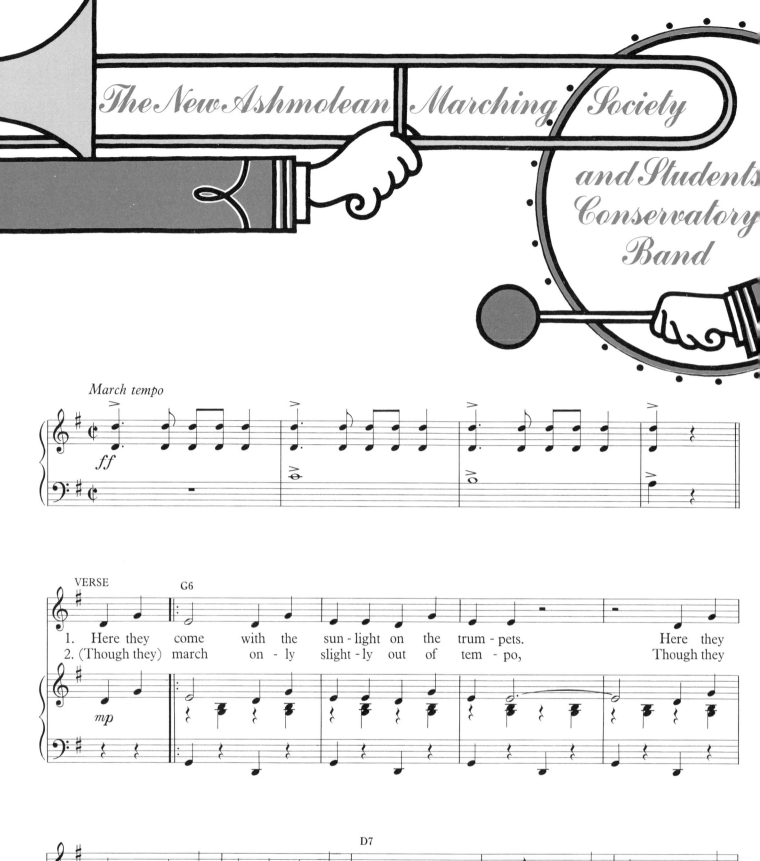

The New Ashmolean Marching Society and Students Conservatory Band

March tempo

ff

VERSE

G6

1. Here they come with the sun-light on the trum-pets. Here they
2. (Though they) march on - ly slight-ly out of tem - po, Though they

mp

D7

come with the ban-ners fly-ing high._____ In my throat I've a
play just a tri-fle out of tune,_____ Though there's just a sug-

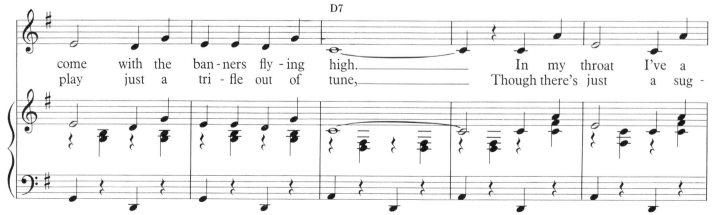

fine Sun - day hat will be high in the air, for the
shout ev - 'ry time at the top of my voice for the

CHORUS

New Ash - mo - le - an March - ing So - ci - e - ty and Stu-dents Con -

ser - va-to - ry band._____
1. Yes, the New Ash - mo - le - an
2. If you're an - a - lyt - i - cal,

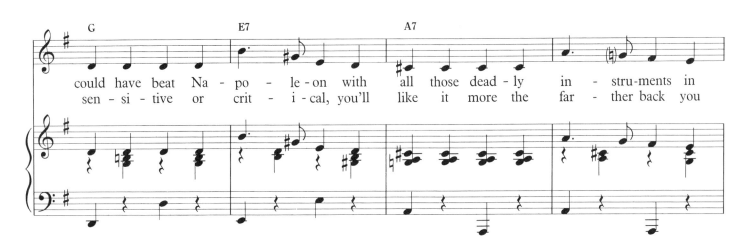

could have beat Na - po - le - on with all those dead - ly in - stru-ments in
sen - si - tive or crit - i - cal, you'll like it more the far - ther back you

76

VERSE

SIR FRANCIS:

'Twas a bright blue sky, And a lark sang high On a bough that was blos-som lad-en,_____ And I had my eye on a

CHORUS

GUYS

A ny story about the production of *Guys and Dolls* almost inevitably ends with a cliché like "The rest is history." The show was the greatest smash hit in the history of the musical theater. It won the New York Critics' Circle and Tony awards, ran twelve hundred performances, grossed twelve million dollars and is still going. At this writing it has been chosen by the National Theatre of England for its first musical production and will star Lord Olivier as Nathan Detroit. The rave notices called the show "The definitive model of flawless musical theater"; "Impossible to top"; "The greatest American musical of all time," etc., etc., etc. It was also a joy to behold, and a perfect example of Frank Loesser's original mind and his ear for idiomatic dialogue.

The working production was also an example of Loesser's ability to work with people until he got what he wanted.

Even though he preferred to write alone musically—"to preserve the exclusivity of failure," he said—he

AND DOLLS

worked with every single member of the cast from those in the largest roles to those in the smallest in his relentless pursuit of perfection, spending hours with people who were only replacements in road companies. And whoever they were, after he worked with them they went away better singers for his pains — confused and terrified, possibly, but better.

Abe Burrows, with whom Loesser had a relationship as friend, collaborator and consistently battling antagonist for thirty years, says (along with some beautiful and glowing words in the eulogy he wrote for *The New York Times*): "When he did funny stuff, outside his work, it was a funny kind of funny. There was the time he stood in the theater and bawled out the entire company, told them exactly how he wanted things and said they were going to rehearse until they got it right. So the company started rehearsing — and suddenly nobody could see Frank. He had walked up the aisle and disappeared, and we all figured he was in a terrible fury. Five minutes later, he strolled back into the theater eating an ice cream cone. You never knew."

Vivian Blaine, the glorious Adelaide of "Adelaide's Lament," also remembers, with deep affection, the Loesser Pursuit of Perfection Syndrome. *Guys and Dolls* was in its fourth week of Philadelphia rehearsals, and everyone was in a state of exhaustion. The show was obviously going to be a hit, but that wasn't good enough for Loesser. The second-act curtain came up on a reprise of "A Bushel and a Peck." It worked well, but Loesser thought it should come up instead on a new song — and he didn't have one. Vivian Blaine watched him fretting about it and said, "Why not dig into the trunk — you must have *something*." Later on, he came to her and said, "Viv, I've got a one-joke song." He sat down at the piano and sang, "He bought me that fur thing five winters ago — " She said, *"What?"* He frowned. "I don't know." She said, "I do. Go on." He fiddled around for a moment, looked her straight in the eye and sang, "Take back your mink..." The next day, costumes were ordered and the number choreographed, and the song went into the show.

The rest, as they say, is history.

GUYS AND DOLLS

Moderato (not too brightly)

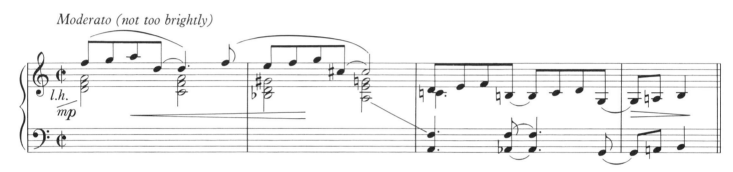

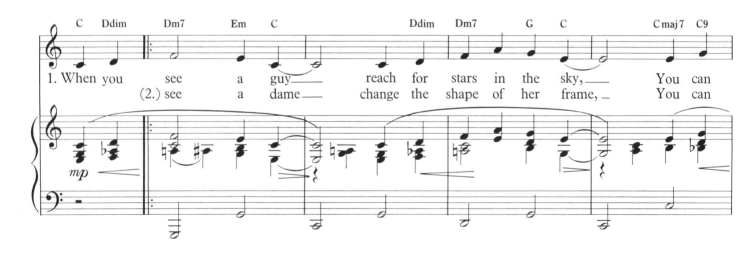

| C | Ddim | Dm7 | Em | C | | Ddim | Dm7 | G | C | Cmaj7 | C9 |

1. When you see a guy____ reach for stars in the sky,____ You can

(2.) see a dame____ change the shape of her frame,_ You can

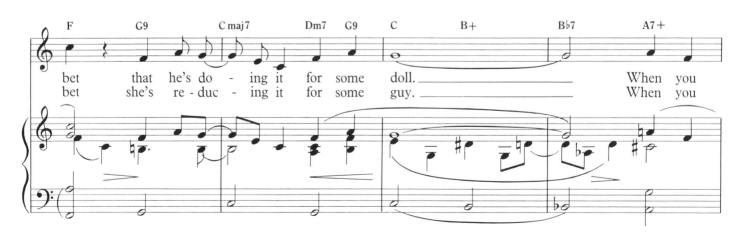

| F | G9 | Cmaj7 | Dm7 | G9 | C | B+ | Bb7 | A7+ |

bet that he's do - ing it for some doll._____ When you

bet she's re - duc - ing it for some guy._____ When you

I'LL KNOW

Moderato

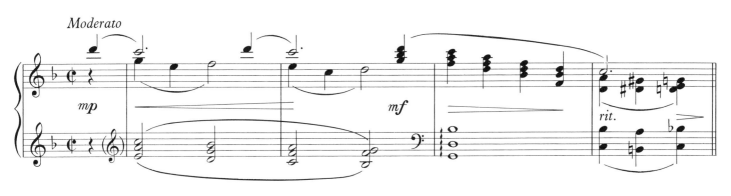

With expression

I'll know when my love comes a-long; I'll know then and

there. I'll know at the sight of {her / his} face How I

87

FUGUE FOR TINHORNS

Steady medium bounce

NICELY: I got the horse right here! The name is Paul Re-vere, And here's a guy that says if the

A BUSHEL AND A PECK

Light bounce tempo

| G | D7 | G | D7 | G | A7 |

I love you a bush-el and a peck, a bush-el and a peck and a
I love you a bush-el and a peck, a bush-el and a peck, tho' you
I love you a bush-el and a peck, a bush-el and a peck, and it

| D | D7 | G | Em7 |

hug a-round the neck, Hug a-round the neck and a bar-rel and a heap,
make my heart a wreck, Make my heart a wreck and you make my life a mess,
beats me all to heck, Beats me all to heck how I'll ev-er tend the farm,

| A7 | D | G9 |

Bar-rel and a heap, and I'm talk-in' in my sleep a-bout
Make my life a mess, yes a mess of hap-pi-ness a-bout
Ev-er tend the farm when I wan-na keep my arm a-bout

IF I WERE A BELL

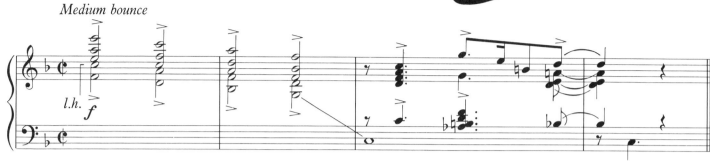

1. Ask me how do I feel; Ask me now that we're co-zy and cling-ing.
(2) how do I feel. From this chem-is-try les-son I'm learn-ing.

Well sir, all I can say is, if I were a bell I'd be
Well sir, all I can say is, if I were a bridge I'd be

ring-ing. From the mo-ment we kissed to-night,
burn-ing. Yes, I knew my mo-rale would crack

ADELAIDE'S LAMENT

The av'rage un - mar - ried fe - male bas - i - c'lly in - se - cure,
fe - male re - main - ing sin - gle, just in the le - gal sense,

Due to some long frus - tra - tion may re - act
Shows a neu - rot - ic ten - den - cy. See note. (Spoken) Note:
With

psy - cho - so - mat - ic symp - toms, dif - fi - cult to en - dure, Af -
Chron - ic or - gan - ic syn - dromes, tox - ic or hy - per - tense, In -

fect - ing the up - per res - pi - ra - tor - y tract. *(Reacting)* In
volv - ing the eye, the ear and the nose and throat. *(Reacting)* In

oth - er words,__ just from wait - ing a - round for that plain lit - tle band of gold, A
oth - er words,__ just from wor - ry - ing wheth - er the wed - ding is on or off, A

per - son__ can de - vel - op a cold. You can
per - son__ can de - vel - op a cough. You can

spray her wher - ev - er you fig - ure the strep - to - coc - ci lurk;__ You can
feed her all day with the vi - ta - min A and the Bro - mo fizz, __ But the

grippe. (Hm!) La grippe. La post - na - sal drip, With the wheez-es and the sneez-es and a

si - nus that's real - ly a pip! From a lack of com - mu - ni - ty prop-er-ty___ and a

feel - ing she's get - ting too old, A per - son___ can de - vel - op a

bad, bad cold.___

MORE I CANNOT WISH YOU

Slowly

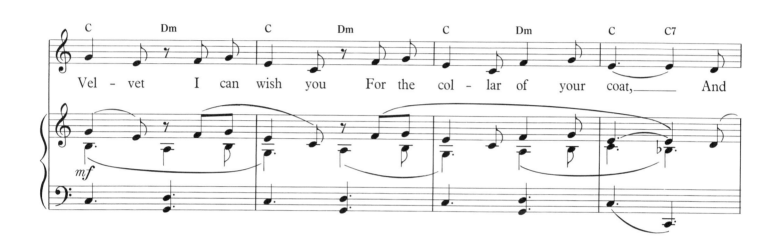

Vel - vet I can wish you For the col - lar of your coat,_____ And

for - tune smil - ing all a - long your way._____ But

more I can - not wish you than to wish you find your love,_____ Your

MY TIME OF DAY

My time of day is the

dark time,___ a cou·ple of deals be·fore dawn, When the street be·longs to the cop___ and the

112

I'VE NEVER BEEN IN LOVE BEFORE

I've nev – er been in love be - fore. Now

113

full of fool - ish song, and out my song must pour. So please for - give this help - less haze I'm in. I've real - ly nev - er been in love be - fore. I've - fore.

115

SIT DOWN YOU'RE ROCKIN' THE BOAT

Freely

mp

Am

C9

1. I dreamed last night I got on the boat to Heav - en, And
(2. I) sailed a - way on that lit - tle boat to Heav - en, And
(3. And) as I laughed at those pas - sen - gers to Heav - en, A

mp

Am

C9

C7+

by some chance I had brought my dice a - long, And
by some chance found a bot - tle in my fist, And
great big wave came and washed me o - ver - board, And

A WOMAN IN LOVE

Romantically

Your eyes are the eyes of a wom-an in love,_____ And oh, how they give you a-way!_____ Why try to de-ny you're a wom-an in love,_____ When I

know ver - y well_____ what I say?_____ _____ I say no moon in the sky ev - er lent such a glow;_____ _____ Some flame deep with - in made them shine._____ Those eyes are the

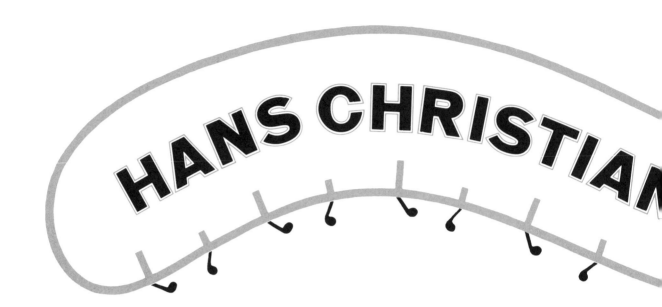

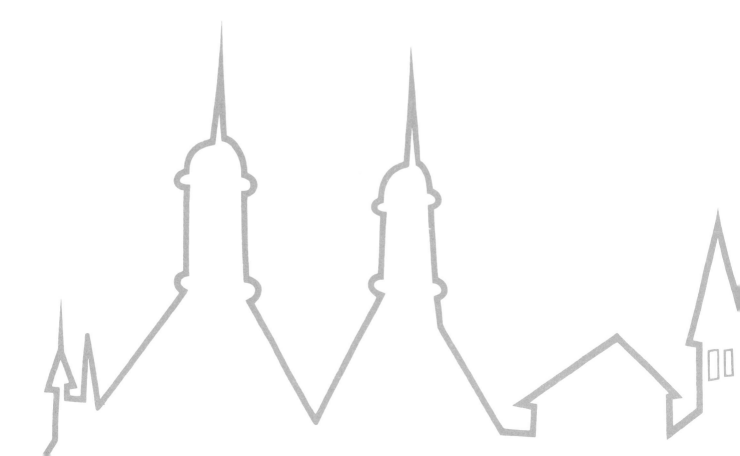

In the midst of writing *The Most Happy Fella*, which was probably closer to Frank Loesser's heart than anything else he ever wrote, he demonstrated not only his extraordinary ability to go on rapidly to something else, but his magic shutoff valve as well. His facets were so many, and his concentration so great, that he could simply turn off one subject or project and turn on another.

Deep in his work on *The Most Happy Fella*, he was called by Samuel Goldwyn to write the score of the motion picture *Hans Christian Andersen*, to star Danny Kaye. Loesser simply shut the lid on *Happy Fella*, went to Hollywood and wrote the delightful score of the film. It was an important score for any film, but unquestionably the greatest score for a children's film ever written. Loesser adored children, and aside from the musicianship of the work, the affection showed. The theme song of the film, "Wonderful Copenhagen," became virtually a second anthem for the Danish people and certainly, for Copenhagen, as important as "Aloha Oe" to the Hawaiians. When Loesser went to Copenhagen some time later, he received an ovation unequaled in the city's history.

There are many beautiful songs in the score, but it is typical of the Loesser character that the principal ballad is sung by the hero not to the heroine, but to an inchworm.

Then he rapidly shut the lid on that scene and went back to *Happy Fella*.

WONDERFUL COPENHAGEN

Valse moderato

Marcato

VERSE

I sail up the Skag-er-rak and sail down the Kat-te-gat through the

har - bor and up to the quay, and there she stands,

waiting for me, With a wel-come so warm and so gay.__

CHORUS *Gemütlich*

Won-der-ful, won-der-ful Co - pen - ha - gen, friend - ly old

girl of a town._____ 'Neath her tav - ern light, on this

mer - ry night, Let us clink and drink one down_____ To

125

THE INCH WORM

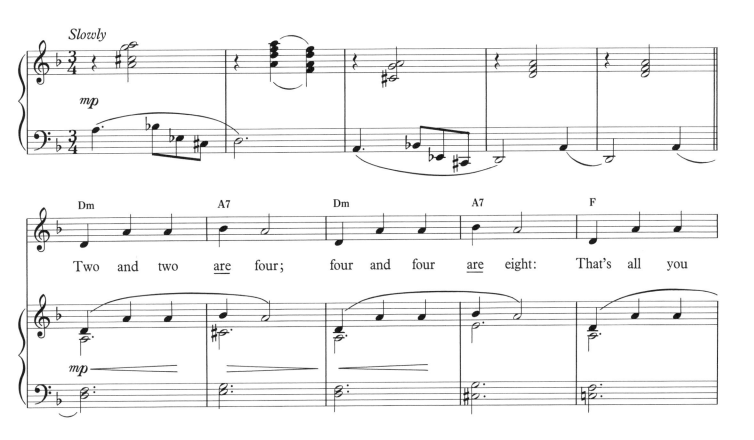

Slowly

mp

| Dm | A7 | Dm | A7 | F |

Two and two are four; four and four are eight: That's all you

mp

127

have on your bus'-ness-like mind. Two and two are four;

four and four are eight. How can you be so blind?

CHORUS

OBBLIGATO

Two and two are four; Four and four are eight;

MELODY

Inch - worm, inch - worm, mea - sur - ing the mar - i - golds,

mp a tempo

128

ANYWHERE I WANDER

Ben marcato

VERSE
Rubato

1. {Her / His} arms were warm as they wel-comed me; {Her / His} eyes were fi - re bright. And
2. {Her / His} voice was, oh, such a soft ca - ress! Of love it gent - ly told. And
3. {Her / His} tears were sil - ver as morn - ing dew As {she / he} bade me good - bye, And

then I knew that my path must be Through the ev - er - haunt - ed night, for
in {her / his} smile was the ten - der - ness I may nev - er - more be - hold, but
ev' - ry tear was a prom - ise true That {her / his} love would nev - er die, so

CHORUS
Ben marcato

An - y -where I wan - der, An - y -where I roam, Till I'm in the arms of my dar - ling a - gain My

tenderly

heart will find no home, _____ An - y -where I wan - der, An - y -where I roam.

2. {Her / His} roam.
3. {Her / His}

131

THUMBELINA

Moderato (lightly)

mp

VERSE
Gdim

Lightly
D7

G

1. Though you're no big - ger than my thumb, ____
(2. Though) you're no big - ger than my toe, ____

mp

D9

G

Gdim

____ Than my thumb, ____ Than my thumb, ____ sweet
____ Than my toe, ____ Than my toe, ____ sweet

133

Thum - be - li - na, what's the dif - f'rence if you're ve - ry small?

When your heart is full of love, you're nine feet tall._____

2. Though nine feet

tall._____

NO TWO PEOPLE

THE UGLY DUCKLING

Lightly, with a waddle

mp

There once was an ug-ly duck-ling with feath-ers all stub-by and brown, and the

oth-er birds, in so man-y words, said, "🌟✗! Get out of town!
(Quack like an angry duck)

🌟✗! Get out, 🌟✗! 🌟✗! get out, 🌟✗! 🌟✗! get out of town!" And he

went, with a quack and a wad-dle and a quack, in a flur-ry of ei - der - down.

That poor lit-tle ug - ly

duck - ling went wan-der-ing far and near, but at ev - 'ry place they

said to his face, "Now, ☀✠‼ get out of here! ☀✠‼ Get out, ☀✠‼

get out, ✺✗!) ✺✗!) get out of here!" And he went, with a quack and a

wad-dle and a quack and a ver - y un-hap-py tear.

All through the win - ter-time he hid him-self a-

way, A-shamed to show his face, A - fraid of what oth - ers might

lake and you'll see!" And he looked and he saw, and he said, "Why, it's me! I am a swan!

Whee! (Sing:) I'm not such an ug-ly duck-ling, No feath-ers all stub-by and

brown." For in fact, these birds, in so man-y words, said, "Tsk!★ the best in

★ (or whistle admiringly)

town! Tsk!★ the best, Tsk,★ Tsk,★ the best, Tsk,★ Tsk,★ the best in

town!"   Not a quack, not a quack, not a wad-dle or a quack, But a

glide and a whis-tle and a snow-y white____ back and a head so no-ble and

high!   "Say, who's an ug-ly duck-ling?   Not I!_____

(Whistle:) _____ (Sing:) Not I!"

Mastering idiomatic dialogue and music was never enough for Frank Loesser. The minute something new was expected of him, no matter how successful his past shows had been, he refused to repeat himself and immediately went farther out and into a different field. Even as critics and public were almost getting used to Loesser's changing themes, he rocked them all back on their heels with something not only he but no one else had done anything like: *The Most Happy Fella*. In publicity for the show, the word "opera" was assiduously avoided, in fear that the public impression would be that it was highbrow. It *was* highbrow, but so carefully handled that the audience wasn't aware of it. As Loesser quoted George S. Kaufman: "Of course be corny — just don't let them catch you at it." So Loesser sneaked what was virtually an opera onto the stage and they didn't catch him at it.

Loesser, although a deeply sentimental person himself, detested oversentimentality onstage; he took as his working slogan "The heart must bleed, not slobber." *The Most Happy Fella* does not slobber, but it does make the heart bleed.

In adapting Sidney Howard's *They Knew What They Wanted* to the musical theater, Loesser bravely turned out a musical with less than fifteen minutes of spoken dialogue. It contained a variety of songs from operatic to musical-comedy to popular, and even included country western.

It was a landmark in the American theater.

In speaking of relations between those involved with the production, conductor Herbert Greene, whom Loesser referred to as a "fat sylph," says: "If you knew Frank Loesser, you were involved. You had no choice, because the man was a genius. Working with him was a mixture of wanting to kiss him or kill him, he was such a mixture of personality opposites. Professionally he was unreasonable, irascible, unfair and infuriating; socially he was gracious, thoughtful, gentle and totally enchanting — the kind of person who would find the most miserable-looking person at a party and go talk to him."

THE MOST HAPPY FELLA

153

STANDING ON THE CORNER

1. Stand - ing on the cor - ner watch-ing all the girls go by,
2. Stand - ing on the cor - ner watch-ing all the girls go by,
3. Stand - ing on the cor - ner watch-ing all the girls go by,

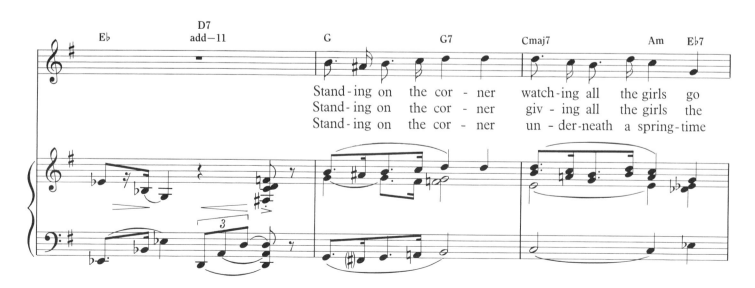

Stand - ing on the cor - ner watch-ing all the girls go
Stand - ing on the cor - ner giv - ing all the girls the
Stand - ing on the cor - ner un - der-neath a spring-time

ABBONDANZA

159

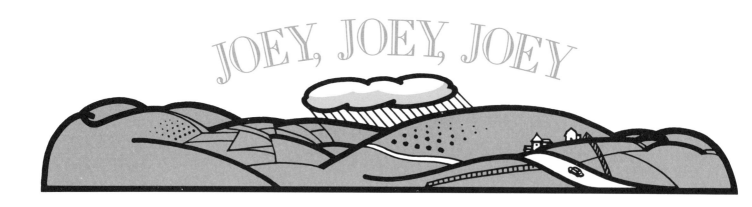

JOEY, JOEY, JOEY

Like a per - fumed wom - an _____ The wind blows in the bunk - house, _____ Like a per - fumed wom - an _____ Smell - in' of where she's

When the grub they've been cook-in' me _____ gets to tast-in' too good, _____ When I've had all I want of the la-dies in the neigh-bor-hood, _____ She sings, "Jo - ey, _____ Jo - ey, Jo - ey, _____ Jo - ey, _____

rall.

L.H.

mp a tempo

HAPPY TO MAKE YOUR ACQUAINTANCE

Freely and lyrically

ROSABELLA: When you meet some-bod-y for the first time, There are spe-cial things you're sup-posed to say, Which you may not mean, but they sound po-lite as can be._____ Would you

BIG **D**

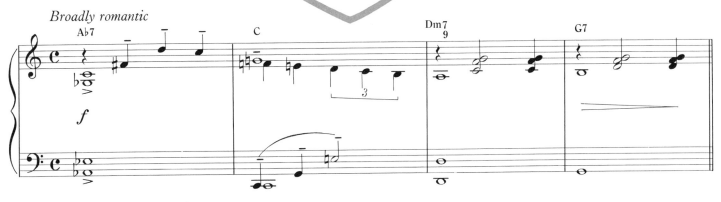

MY HEART IS SO FULL OF YOU

Broadly romantic

My heart is so full of you, so full of

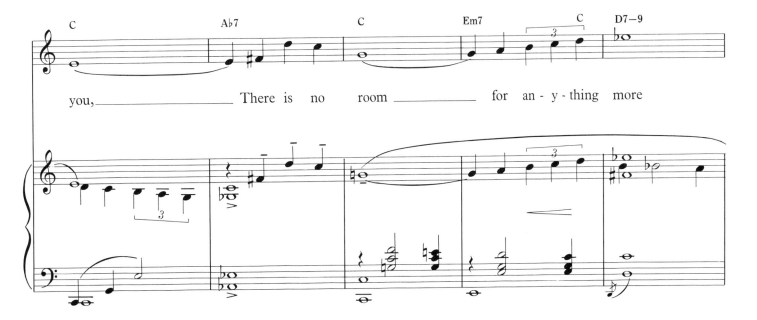

you,_____ There is no room_____ for an-y-thing more

G*reenwillow* was one of Frank Loesser's great loves and great disappointments. He had read B. J. Chute's novel *Greenwillow* with admiration and affection. The decision to try to translate the delicate, almost cobweblike content of the book to the more solid musical-comedy idiom was a tough one. But all anyone had to tell Frank Loesser was that he could not do something to ensure that he would go ahead and do it.

After he made the decision to go ahead with *Greenwillow,* he proceeded with caution and regard for the original property, maintaining the wistfulness and nostalgia of the novel in the libretto he wrote with Lesser Samuels.

For Frank Loesser, whose dictum had often been "Loud is good," to write a quiet, gentle, mystical score like that of *Greenwillow* was a total turnabout from what was expected of him, and the critics and public, unaware that the only thing to expect from him was the unexpected, were not ready for it.

Joy Chute, the author of the original property, says of the production of *Greenwillow*: "I was a cross between a masseuse and a tea cozy during production: everybody's neck and psyche needed comforting. Frank wanted so badly for the show to be great—for everybody, not for himself. Getting credit never bothered him; he just wanted to do it, and do it right. The show's lack of success was disappointing, but if nothing at all had come of it, it would have been worth it because just knowing Frank would have been enough." From an *author?*

Frank Loesser was in London the night the show closed after ninety-five performances. Instead of the usual closing notice to the cast, he simply cabled: OOOPS—SORRY.

The Music of Home

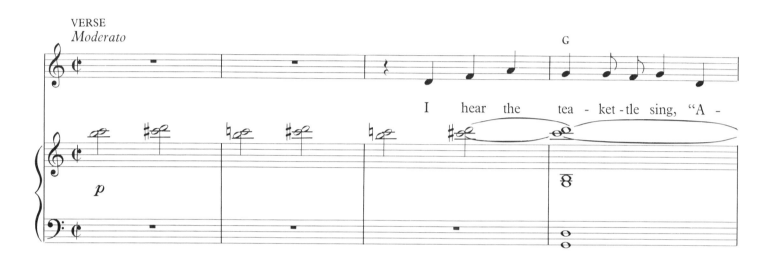

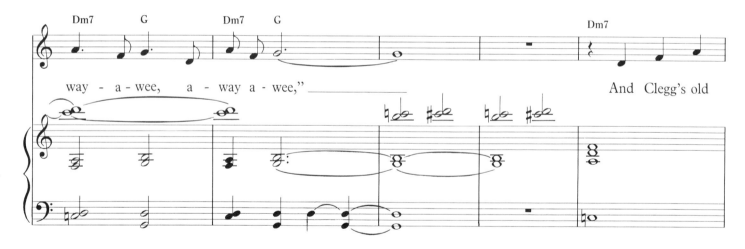

hav - ing at a game,_____

Slower and flowingly

And the voice of one I dear - ly

love call - ing my name._____

CHORUS

'Tis the mu - sic of home, the mu - sic of

Summertime Love

VERSE
Freely (recitative)

I've been told, I've been told by the wise and the old, _____ Some-thing good I'm sup-posed to re-mem-ber: _____ If my first love I've found in the warm of Ju-ly, It-'ll cool in the nip of Sep-tem-ber. _____ Now they

point to the skies, do the old and the wise,____ And they speak of a chill in the

air, And they wink while they're nudg - ing me o - ver to the

In tempo (bright)

pret - ty lit - tle la - dies in the square._____

_____ But I don't care,____ For

CHORUS

Still I love my sum - mer - time love. _____ Still I love the kiss - ing _____ and the court - ing. _____ Still I love my sum - mer - time love _____ With a heart still

up through the crack in the floor_____ And still I

love_____ my sum - mer - time love._____

Still I love the

kiss - ing_____ and the court - ing._____

189

Greenwillow Christmas

Moderato

SOPRANO / ALTO

1. Three wise men fol-lowed a star one night to
2. 'Twas long a-go in___ Beth-le-hem, yet

TENOR / BASS

2nd time—unis.

Hum ___

where glad bells were peal-ing___ And soon be-held the___
ev-er lives the glo-ry,___ And hearts all glow and

2nd time *Ah* ___

div.
Hum ___ *Ah* ___ *Hum* ___
unis.

Never W

VERSE *Recitative*

An - y flim - sy dim - sy look - ing for true love ____

____ Bet - ter smile me no "Good dear - ie, good day." ____

I Marry

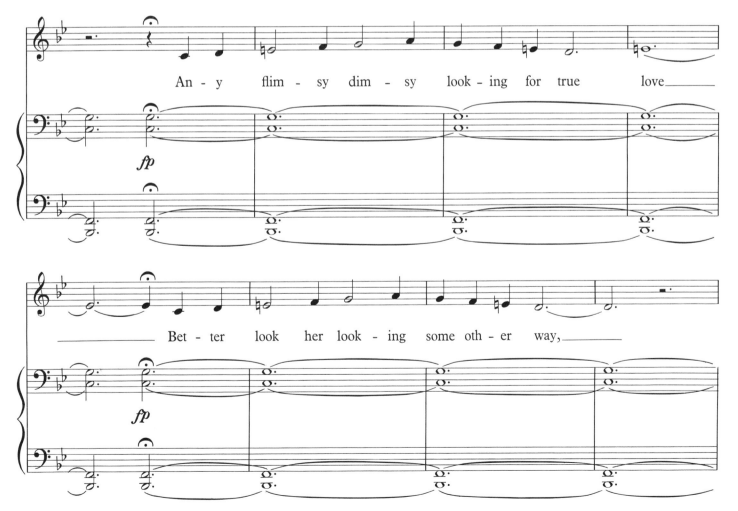

An - y flim - sy dim - sy look - ing for true love_____

_____ Bet - ter look her look - ing some oth - er way,_____

For my kiss can be no ev - er - more prom - ise, But a fan - cy dan - cy fid - dle and free. An - y flim - sy dim - sy look - ing for true love Bet - ter waste no time, no time on me.

Along with friends' slapping their thighs and roaring, "That's a Frank!" after some outrageous anecdote about Frank Loesser, another phrase, "Nobody but Frank could have —," consistently crops up. Certainly no one but Loesser could have knocked out the score of a musical comedy that was a deliberate piece of beautifully constructed nonsense and receive a Pulitzer Prize for it.

The show, adapted from a book by Shepherd Mead, was *How to Succeed in Business Without Really Trying*. Loesser, who wrote the music, and Abe Burrows, who directed the show and wrote the script with Jack Weinstock and Willie Gilbert, both received the prize.

It took Loesser four weeks to write the score, and he had another hit. The whole show wore a grin across it. A wicked satire on the business world and businessmen, it made an absurdity of the common daily fault of taking oneself seriously. An organ plays solemnly as an executive marches into a conference room; a girl sings that she would be "Happy to Keep His Dinner Warm" while her intended climbs to the top of the business world (a neat accomplishment, as he has just been promoted from the mail room); a rousing "Riff Song"-type number called "Brotherhood of Man" is belted out by the company, the words of which demonstrate that the brothers are dedicated only to undoing one another; and — joy of joys — the hit song of the show, "I Believe in You," is sung by the hero not to the heroine, but to *himself* in the mirror, with the glorious amplified accompaniment in the background of musicians singing into kazoos to sound like an electric razor.

How to Succeed was a flawless example of Loesser's directive to young composers: "Remember, a song is like a freight train moving across a stage. Every boxcar has a word on it. Those people have to hear everything and understand it — fast, because in a minute the car will be gone and they'll never see it again. Make them listen and then *lay it in their laps*."

HOW TO SUCCEED IN BUSINESS WITHOUT REALLY TRYING

WORLD WIDE WICKETS

I BELIEVE IN YOU

Yet there's that slam - bang tang rem - i -

nis - cent of gin and ver - mouth.

Oh, I be - lieve in you,_____ I be - lieve in

you._____

THE COMPANY WAY

VERSE
Rubato

TWIMBLE:

When I joined this firm _____ as a brash young man, _____ "Well," I said to my-self, "now, brash young man, don't get an-y i – deas." Well, I stuck to that, and I

Breezily, in tempo

haven't had one in years!

FINCH: *(Spoken)*
You play it safe!

CHORUS
TWIMBLE: *(Sung)*
I play it the com-pa-ny way.___ Wher-

ev-er the com-pa-ny puts me, there I'll stay.
FINCH:
But

what is your point___ of view?
TWIMBLE:
I have no point of view!
FINCH:
Sup-

F.
Bb7 TWIMBLE: Db9 C7 FINCH: Fm Fm+7
ni - ture? Oh, it suits me fine. The com - pa - ny let -
Fm7 TWIMBLE: F+ Bb7 Eb FINCH: (Spoken) Db9
ter head is... A val - en - tine! Is there an - y - thing you're a -
Gb6 TWIMBLE: Db7 FINCH: (Sung) Gb Abm7
gainst? Un - em - ploy - ment! When they want bril - liant think - ing from em -
fp sfz p sfz p
Db7 Gb6 TWIMBLE: Eb Db9 F+ Db7 FINCH:
ploy - ees? That is no con - cern of mine. Sup - pose a
sfz p

HAPPY TO KEEP HIS DINNER WARM

I'll be so Hap-py to keep his din-ner warm_____ while he goes

on - ward____ and up - ward.____

Hap-py to keep his din-ner warm_____ till he comes wea-ri-ly home__ from down-

town. I'll be there wait-ing un-til his mind is clear_____

_____ while he looks through me,__ right through me,__

Wait-ing to say, "Good eve-ning, dear._____ I'm preg-nant.

wear - ing the wife - ly u - ni - form _____ while he goes

on - ward ____ and up - ward. ___

Hap - py to keep his din - ner warm _____ till he comes

wea - ri - ly home ____ from down - town. _____

219

BROTHERHOOD OF MAN

With a handclapper spiritual feeling

There is a broth-er-hood_____ of man,

A_____ be-nev-o-lent broth-er-hood_____ of

man, A no-ble tie that binds__

proud to be____ in that fra - ter - ni - ty,____ The great big

broth - er - hood of man?____

There is a man?____

INDEX OF FIRST LINES

(For those songs having a separate verse,
the line given is the first line of the chorus.)

INDEX OF SONGS